For Aslang Nødset

GO AWAY, DOG
Text copyright © 1963 by Joan L. Nodset
Pictures copyright © 1963 by Crosby Newell Bonsall
Printed in the United States of America. All rights reserved.
LIBRARY OF CONGRESS CATALOG CARD NUMBER: 63-11162

by JOAN L. NODSET

Away, Dog

pictures by Crosby Bonsall

HARPER & ROW, PUBLISHERS
NEW YORK, EVANSTON, and LONDON

Go away, you bad old dog.
Go away from me.
I don't like you, dog.

I don't like dogs at all.
Big dogs, little dogs.
Any dogs at all.

I don't want that stick.
Don't give it to me.

If I throw the stick,
will you go away?

There now, go away with your stick.

What do you want now?

If I throw it again,
will you go away?

Don't jump on me, dog.
I don't like that.

Go away, you old dog.
Go on home now.

Don't you have a home?
Well, that's too bad.
But you can't come home with me.

Don't wag your tail at me.
I don't like dogs.

You aren't bad for a dog.
But I don't like dogs.

Say, do that again.
Roll over again, dog.
Say, that's not bad.

Can you shake hands?
This is how to shake hands.

I didn't say to lick my hand.
Stop that, you old dog.

If I play with you, will you go away?

All right, let's run, dog.
Can you run as fast as I can?

You can run fast all right.

That was fun, dog.
Maybe we can play again.

But I have to go home now.
No, you can't come.
Go away now, dog.

Don't look so sad, dog.
Don't look that way at me.
Can I help it if you don't have a home?

Why don't you go away?

You like me, don't you, you old dog?
Well, I like you, too.

All right, I give up.

Come on home, dog.
Come on, let's run.